Jumping the Gun

The Spirals Series

Fiction

Jim Alderson
The Witch Princess

Jan Carew
Death Comes to the Circus
Footprints in the Sand
Voices in the Dark

Barbara Catchpole
Laura Called
Nick

Susan Duberley
The Ring

Keith Fletcher and Susan Duberley
Nightmare Lake

John Goodwin
Dead-end Job
Ghost Train

Angela Griffiths
Diary of a Wild Thing

Marian Iseard
Loved to Death

Anita Jackson
The Actor
The Austin Seven
Bennet Manor
Dreams
The Ear
A Game of Life and Death
No Rent to Pay

Paul Jennings
Eye of Evil
Maggot

Helen Lowerson
The Biz

Margaret Loxton
The Dark Shadow

Patrick Nobes
Ghost Writer

David Orme
City of the Roborgs
The Haunted Asteroids

Kevin Philbin
Summer of the Werewolf

Bill Ridgway
Jack's Video
Mr Punch

Julie Taylor
Spiders

John Townsend
Back on the Prowl
Beware the Morris Minor
Fame and Fortune
Night Beast
A Minute to Kill
Snow Beast

Non-fiction

Jim Alderson
Crash in the Jungle

David Orme
Hackers

Bill Ridgway
Lost in Alaska

Julie Taylor
Lucky Dip

John Townsend
Burke and Hare: The Body Snatchers
SOS

Plays

Jan Carew
Computer Killer
No Entry

Julia Donaldson
Books and Crooks

John Godfrey
When I Count to Three

Angela Griffiths
Wally and Co

Paul Groves
Tell Me Where it Hurts

Barbara Mitchelhill
Punchlines
The Ramsbottoms at Home

Bill Ridgway
Monkey Business

John Townsend
A Bit of a Shambles
Breaking the Ice
Cheer and Groan
Clogging the Works
Cowboys, Jelly and Custard
Hanging by a Fred
Hiccups and Slip-ups
Jumping the Gun
The Lighthouse Keeper's Secret
A Lot of Old Codswallop
Making a Splash
Over and Out
Rocking the Boat
Spilling the Beans
Taking the Plunge

David Walke
The Good, the Bad and the Bungle
Package Holiday

NEW **Spirals**

Jumping the Gun

John Townsend

This book
belongs to

First published in 2001 by:
Nelson Thornes Ltd
Delta Place
27 Bath Road
CHELTENHAM
GL53 7TH
United Kingdom

01 02 03 04 05 / 10 9 8 7 6 5 4 3 2 1

A catalogue record for this book is available from the British Library.

ISBN 0-7487-6064-4

Cover artwork by Harry Venning
Typeset by Tech-Set, Gateshead
Printed and bound in Great Britain by Martins The Printers Ltd, Berwick upon Tweed

Contents

A play of three acts for four parts.

Ted Plunge

Edna Plunge

Thug

Anna Bruce (a TV presenter)

Clearing the Decks _____ 6

Plugging the Gaps _____ 18

Treading the Boards _____ 29

Clearing the Decks

Scene: Ted and Edna are in a beach hut by the sea. Ted sits in a deckchair looking out at the storm while Edna spring-cleans the beach hut.

Ted	It's right nippy, Edna.
Edna	They said it would get colder.
Ted	Pretty windy, too.
Edna	A cold front.
Ted	It's my back that's chilly.
Edna	That's what the weather man said on the telly. A cold front, wet patches and terrible wind.
Ted	They shouldn't let him on the telly if he's like that.
Edna	He said something about lots of ice bars.
Ted	I'd rather have a hot chocolate. It's like winter.
Edna	He said something big was coming down from the north.
Ted	Let's hope it's not your sister on the bus! You can never trust what the weather man says, anyway.

Edna	I think he's very nice. It's a shame about his ears. They blot out the whole of Wales.
Ted	I wish they'd let Anna Bruce do the weather.
Edna	Your heart-throb who reads the News!
Ted	She'd make me feel much warmer. The sea's rough.
Edna	Cup of tea, Ted?
Ted	I'd rather have a Lemsip.
Edna	Have you got a cold coming?
Ted	It's already moved in. I've got a cold everything.
Edna	I'll light the gas for the kettle.
Ted	A nip of rum would help. Look at the spray.
Edna	So you're not going in for a dip?
Ted	Don't be silly, dear.
Edna	The sea would do you good. It would kill that cold of yours.
Ted	It would kill all of me, Edna. Just look at it. It's freezing.
Edna	It's just a bit fresh, that's all.
Ted	It's rough, it's grey, it's angry, it's . . . Edna, I think it's coming this way. Look at the size of those waves!
Edna	It's cosy to watch the tide coming in from our beach hut.

Ted	It's more than coming in. It looks like it's staying the night.
Edna	Just take lots of deep breaths. Blow away the cobwebs.
Ted	More like pickle my lungs.
Edna	This sea air does you a lot of good.
Ted	How can you be so sure?
Edna	Have you ever seen a dead seagull?
Ted	No, I don't think so.
Edna	There you are, then. What's good for seagulls is good for us.
Ted	My throat feels bad – just like I've licked the whole beach.
Edna	Have a look in my handbag. You'll find some of that smelly stuff to rub on your chest.
Ted	[*Looking in Edna's handbag*] Oh yes, I've got it. It smells pretty strong – like pear drops. There we are, I'll rub it in all over. Is it meant to do this?
Edna	What are you doing?
Ted	I've gone a funny colour.
Edna	That's my nail varnish, Ted. You look like a robin on a Christmas card!
Ted	My vest has gone pink. It smells terrible.

Edna	Spray some air freshener on it. There's a can in my bag.
Ted	The air is already fresh. Look at everything blowing about.
Edna	What are you doing, Ted?
Ted	Spraying my chest to get rid of the smell.
Edna	But that's my hair spay you're using.
Ted	My vest has set solid!
Edna	That hair spray is no good, anyway. Throw it in the dustbin.
Ted	Why have you got a dustbin in the beach hut?
Edna	I'm cleaning up. Anyway, it would blow away outside.
Ted	Are you trying to clear the decks?
Edna	You know how I like to tidy things up. I was mopping the floor while you were asleep.
Ted	I wasn't asleep. I saw you.
Edna	I scrubbed the step while you had a nap.
Ted	I didn't have a nap. I saw you.
Edna	I wiped the shelf while you had a kip.
Ted	I didn't have a kip. I saw you.
Edna	I washed the door while you had a snooze.
Ted	I didn't have a snooze. I saw you.

Edna	I did a tap dance in a grass skirt with a bucket on my head and a stick of rock up my nose while you had forty winks.
Ted	I didn't have forty winks. I saw you. You did what?
Edna	Ha! I caught you out! Anyway, I've got proof you were asleep. I took a photo – smile! [*FLASH*] You look so cosy.
Ted	Cosy? There's a force-ten gale whizzing through my vest, the roof is creaking like mad and it's like sitting in a fridge.
Edna	But it's ours, Ted. For two more days. I've always wanted to sit in a beach hut on holiday. We've got all we need.
Ted	We haven't got a Lemsip.
Edna	A gas ring . . . a telly . . . a kettle and a tap. And I've been making pastry for my jam puffs.
Ted	The last jam puff you made is on the rockery in the garden.
Edna	This pastry is lighter. I've put in more lard.
Ted	That will just make it waterproof. I could do with your pastry for fixing the gutter at home. Just the job. Like putty.
Edna	My jam puffs are very nice. So is this holiday. It's doing us good, Ted. Stand at the door and

10

take three deep breaths. That will cure your cold. I'll take a photo.

Ted   [*He stands at the door and takes three deep breaths. On the third, he gets soaked just as Edna takes a photo*] Edna, I'm soaked!

Edna   Well, it saves you getting undressed to go in for a swim! The sea has come to you – it must have been tired of waiting for you! Tell you what, let's close the door.

Ted   It will be a bit dark in here.

Edna   It's pretty dark out there, too. Come on, we'll have a cup of tea, cuddle up and watch a bit of telly.

Ted   [*Closing the door*] We could have stayed at home for that.

Edna   Yes, but sea air is good for you. I'll put on the light. It was a good idea of yours to bring a car battery to rig up the light and telly. It's just the job.

Ted   Is it time for the News? I hope it's Anna Bruce today. She'll make me feel better.

Edna   You never hear the News. All you do is sit and stare at her.

Ted   She's lovely. I go weak at the knees whenever she comes on the telly.

Edna	Ooh, Ted – you old softy. [*She switches on the television*]
Ted	It's not a very good picture.
Edna	There's a bad hum.
Ted	More of a buzz.
Edna	It must be the weather. It's a bad signal.
Ted	I'll wiggle the aerial. Any better?
Edna	A bit. It's gone snowy. Hold it up in the air.
Ted	The buzzing is worse over here.
Edna	No wonder, dear. There's a wasp in the sugar.
Ted	Then I'll poke it out with the aerial . . .
Edna	Stop! That's it! Keep it there. Perfect. Yes, she's on. It's Anna Bruce.
Ted	I can't quite see from here. Has she got a new hair style?
Edna	No, dear. That's a map of Africa.
Ted	I can't keep the aerial like this for long.
Edna	She's in that green dress. The one you like.
Ted	Turn up the telly. I want to hear her voice.
Edna	She's saying something about a robbery. Sacks of money were stolen last night from a van. A Group Ten van.
Ted	I can't stand over here all day.

12

Edna	The woman driver was kidnapped. They think the armed gang left the country in a boat. With ten million pounds!
Ted	If they're out in a boat in this weather, they won't get far.
Edna	Ooh, quick, Ted. It's the end of the News.
Ted	Come over and hold the aerial so I can see her.
Edna	Where shall I hold it?
Ted	Up there. Stand on the chair.
Edna	Hurry up, she's about to say 'goodbye'.
Ted	I go all wobbly when she winks at the end of the News. I like to think she's saying 'goodbye' just to me.
Edna	That wasp is on the jam now.
Ted	Don't poke it with the aerial!
Edna	I don't want a wasp in the jam.
Ted	I don't want Anna to go fuzzy. Keep it still.
Edna	It's dive-bombing the butter.
Ted	Now her face has gone fat with lots of lines.
Edna	Mine went like that years ago!
Ted	Hold up that aerial, Edna. She's about to say 'goodbye'.
Edna	I can't. The wasp is on the war path.

Ted	That's perfect. Stay still. She's just right. Goodnight, Anna.
Edna	Can I get down now?
Ted	Not yet. It's the weather.
Edna	Well, we know about the weather. It's in a bad mood. That's why we're shut in here. Listen to that rain on the roof.
Ted	There's a flood warning.
Edna	No wonder that wasp has come inside.
Ted	Extra high tides. Ooh, hold on! They said people by the sea must listen carefully . . .
Edna	Aaah! It's in my hair.
Ted	Now look what you've done! I've lost the sound again.
Edna	I could lose my ear! It's on my head. Hit it, will you?
Ted	You want me to hit your head?
Edna	With a newspaper. Quick.
Ted	Have we got any fly spray?
Edna	You're not going to spray my head!
Ted	Where's that hair spray, then?
Edna	What good will that do?
Ted	It will starch the wasp to death.

14

Edna	Pass up the dustbin lid. I need a shield.
Ted	[*Hitting out with a newspaper*] Did I get it?
Edna	I don't know where it went. I don't like it up here.
Ted	Do that again.
Edna	What?
Ted	Touch your glasses and lift that leg in the air.
Edna	Why?
Ted	The picture on the telly is perfect when you do that.
Edna	What happens if I do this? [*Holding the dustbin lid high over her head*]
Ted	Blimey! You've just picked up Sky!
Edna	How do you mean?
Ted	With that dustbin lid in the air, you're like a dish. We're picking up loads of channels. Lots of them are foreign.
Edna	I'm dizzy up here.
Ted	I've got an idea. If I rig that aerial and lid in the roof, we'll pick up the lot. I'll do it right now.
Edna	Now? Can't it wait?
Ted	You know what I'm like when I get a bee in my bonnet.
Edna	A bit like me when I get a wasp in my whatnot.

Ted	I could fix it just up there in the ceiling.
Edna	There's a trap door thing. There must be a bit of loft space.
Ted	I can easily get up there. I can move the table just like this.
Edna	What was that?
Ted	What?
Edna	That noise. And a shudder. It made me go all funny.
Ted	It was only me moving the table.
Edna	No, there it was again. What's that creaking? You're swaying up and down. Ted, keep still.
Ted	That hair spray must have got to you. I expect you're just a bit dizzy. Nothing to worry about.
Edna	Why is the chair slipping about?
Ted	Just pass it up here on the table. Then I can get into the roof.
Edna	Ted, my feet are wet.
Ted	Mine aren't. The rest of me is wet but not my feet.
Edna	That's because you're standing on the table.
Ted	I think I can just about pull myself up to the trap door.
Edna	I've just had a thought.

Ted	Yes, I've got myself up here. It's very dark. Lots of rubbish.
Edna	I'm paddling down here.
Ted	I'll have to clear the decks and make a bit of room.
Edna	Things are sliding off the shelf. I've gone ever-so wobbly.
Ted	Oh heck. Blimey.
Edna	The only time I feel like this is when I'm in a boat.
Ted	Deary me.
Edna	I'll have to open the door to get some fresh air. [*Opens door*] Oh heck. Blimey. Deary me.
Ted	You won't believe this, Edna.
Edna	You won't believe this, Ted.
Ted	There's a body up here.
Edna	We've been washed out to sea.
Ted	We've got a corpse.
Edna	We've got a floating beach hut.
Ted	What do we do now?
Edna	There's only one thing we can do.
Ted	What's that?
Edna	I'll just have to take a photo. [*FLASH*] After all, everyone will be so amazed. No one will believe me when I show them!

Plugging the Gaps

Scene: Ted and Edna are at sea in a beach hut. Ted is in the roof with a body.

Edna	My slippers are sopping wet. They're full of sea water. I'm sure it's getting deeper.
Ted	I'm bringing the body down, Edna. Ouch, I've torn my vest!
Edna	It's up to my ankles. I've heard of rising damp but not this.
Ted	I've come over all dizzy. My vest is twisting round my neck. We're rocking up and down and sideways. So is my vest.
Edna	If I open the door to throw water out, the sea comes in.
Ted	Can you see land, dear?
Edna	I can't see anything out there – only waves. My glasses are all steamed up.
Ted	So is my vest. I think it's about to rip to shreds.
Edna	Ted, we're sinking. It's just like that sad film we saw.
Ted	I've never seen a sad film about a vest ripping to shreds.

18

Edna	No, dear. That film where they sink after hitting an iceberg.
Ted	This is a beach hut. Titanic was a great ship full of fine things.
Edna	Well I've got jam puffs on board! What was that thud? I hope it wasn't an iceberg.
Ted	It's this body. My vest is giving way.
Edna	Ooh, Ted, his eyes – I'm sure he just gave me a wink!
Ted	By heck, I heard him give a grunt.
Edna	It looks like he's cut himself. There's a plaster over his mouth.
Ted	I'll let him down by his braces. Hold the table steady. There's a nasty bump on his head.
Edna	Water is still coming up through the little holes in the floor.
Ted	I think he needs a doctor.
Edna	I think we need a plumber. I've got just the thing to plug up all the gaps in the planks. My pastry!
Ted	He's got a sack in his hand. There's something in it.
Edna	My pastry is good putty. It's stopping the water coming in.

Ted	His hands are tied up. That's odd . . .
Edna	That's better. Now we're sea-worthy. No one will believe us when we tell them about this. I've got to have proof. Where's the video camera?
Ted	On that shelf. By gum, this chap is heavy.
Edna	Let me film you giving him the kiss of life. [*She uses the video camera*]
Ted	After all that garlic in the curry last night, it could be the kiss of death!
Edna	Let me try my first aid. The first thing you have to do is check.
Ted	Check what?
Edna	Check for danger.
Ted	We're in a beach hut out at sea. How's that for danger?
Edna	Then you have to tap him and say 'hello'.
Ted	Why's that?
Edna	To see if he's awake. To see if there's a reply.
Ted	All right, then. Here goes . . . Hello. Can you hear me?
Edna	Give him a tap.
Ted	Right . . . oops – sorry.

Edna	That was more than a tap. That was a poke in the eye.
Ted	I'm not very good at this, am I?
Edna	There's a first-aid kit here somewhere. And I always carry an onion in my handbag. [*She puts the video camera back*]
Ted	In case you come across a hot-dog in need?
Edna	I always rub an onion on bites and stings. Just the job.
Ted	Put it under his nose. It might bring him round.
Edna	Not till we've done our ABC.
Ted	Our ABC?
Edna	The ABC of first aid. A is for airway – yes, it's clear. B is for breathing – yes, the chest is moving. C is for . . . let me think . . .
Ted	Cycle clips? Take off his cycle clips.
Edna	Those aren't cycle clips. They're handcuffs.
Ted	On his feet?
Edna	And it's not a him, it's a her.
Ted	In jacket, trousers, shirt and tie?
Edna	She's in uniform. In fact she looks a bit like Anna Bruce.

Ted	Then I'd better give her the kiss of life!
Edna	No need, Ted. She's waking up.
Ted	Look what it says on her tie – 'Group Ten'.
Edna	The woman driver – the one on the News. She was driving a Group Ten van when she was kidnapped by robbers.
Ted	Poor woman. We'll have to get her an ambulance.
Edna	More like a life boat. What else did you see up in the roof?
Ted	Just a load of sacks. And an old sleeping bag.
Edna	Anyone in it?
Ted	Not sure.
Edna	There could be robbers up there lying low.
Ted	You can't lie low in a roof.
Thug	[*Dropping down between them and waving a gun*] SHUT IT!
Edna	Told you, Ted.
Ted	Well I never.
Thug	Oi, did you hear me?
Edna	That's not very polite, young man.
Thug	I said, SHUT IT!
Edna	Have you been asleep up there?

22

Thug	FREEZE!
Ted	Telling me, it's right chilly.
Thug	I said, FREEZE!
Ted	You're like me, you need another vest.
Thug	FREEEEEEEZE!
Edna	If you're that cold, love, there's a blanket here.
Thug	Don't move. I've got you covered.
Ted	You're the one who needs to be covered if you're so cold.
Edna	It's a nice thick blanket. You'll soon warm up.
Thug	FREEZE. You're both covered.
Edna	I know. It's fluff from that blanket. It gets all over the place.
Thug	Move again and I'll pull the trigger.
Edna	Cup of tea? I was just about to put the kettle on.
Ted	This poor lady could do with a cup. She was knocked out . . .
Thug	Listen, mate – it was me who knocked her out and I'll do the same to you – know what I mean?
Edna	Do you take sugar?
Thug	Listen, you old bag – I'll blast you into the sky if you don't shut up. This gun is loaded.

Ted	It looks like he doesn't want sugar, Edna.
Edna	He's very rude. You won't get a biscuit if you speak like that.
Thug	SHUT UP! You old fools are in the middle of big trouble. If you poke your nose in a wasp's nest, you get stung.
Edna	Oh yes, talking of wasps, one was in here somewhere . . .
Thug	So now you've been stupid enough to poke your fat noses into my hideout, you'll get stung all right. You'll get DEAD!
Ted	We could always pretend we haven't seen you!
Thug	Too late. The money, the guns and the hostage are getting picked up by boat at high tide. But now you know too much.
Edna	High tide? There's something you need to know . . .
Thug	SHUT IT! You're doing my head in. Go and stand in the corner where I'll shoot you in the head. I've already shot the rest of my gang. I get what I want – know what I mean?
Edna	How about a jam puff?
Ted	They've only just been made.
Thug	Get it into your thick heads – you're dead meat. I kill anyone who gets in my way. I shoot old

	fools like you. Have you got that into your feeble brains?
Ted	Edna's jam puffs are very nice.
Thug	Listen, mate – climb back up in the roof. I've left one more sack up there. If you don't bring it down in ten seconds, you'll be full of shot. Got it?
Ted	Up in the roof? Again? I get dizzy.
Thug	MOVE!
Ted	[*He stands on the table*] I feel a bit wobbly.
Thug	Hurry. I've got a boat coming. I'll have ten million pounds all to myself. You'll be dead just as I start to live. I'll be out on the sea – after being stuck up in the roof for ten hours.
Edna	All that time? You must be peckish. Are you sure I can't press you to a nice fresh jam puff?
Ted	Aaah! [*He hangs by his braces*] I'm sort of stuck.
Thug	That's it! I've had enough. You stupid old fool. You idiot, you dope head, block head [*thumping the table with each insult*], numskull, dip head, dumbell, pea brain, fat head, thick head, bone head, clod head . . . I HATE YOU!
Edna	Mind your language, young man.
Ted	And mind that table.

Thug	[*Shouting angrily*] I hate you and your naf beach hut. I hate your stupid tin-pot world with its cups of tea and jam puffs. This world is full of boring old twits like you who do nothing!
Ted	We're on holiday.
Thug	I want power, freedom and money. I want to be cool. That's why I kill – why I'm about to mow you down and wipe you out. I'm tough. I'm smart. I've got bottle.
Edna	I bet you haven't got the nerve to eat a whole jam puff.
Thug	SHUT UP! Why aren't you shaking with fear? I'll show you who's boss. I'll make you beg me for mercy. And yes, you stupid old crow – I'll easily eat one of your damn puffs.
Edna	JAM puffs. No need to swear.
Thug	But you won't see me finish it. You know why? You'll both be dead. I shoot on the word 'go'. On your marks . . . get set . . . [*He bites a chunk of jam puff*] . . . g . . .

[*BANG! The gun fires into the floor. Water squirts up. Ted falls onto the thug, knocking the gun to the floor. Edna takes a photo. The body on the table sits up.*]

Edna	Ted, you jumped the gun just in time – and I've got a photo.

Ted	By gum, Edna, that was a close shave. I'd better get rid of his gun. [*He throws it out the door as water sprays in*]
Thug	[*Rolling around on the floor*] Aargh . . . ughmph . . . grrrrr . . .
Edna	Just look at him – no manners.
Ted	He's foaming at the mouth.
Edna	It can't be my jam puff. They're fresh.
Thug	Can't breath. Die. Throat. Pain. Wasp. Ugh errrrrrrrr . . .
Edna	I wondered where that wasp went. It was in the jam puff!
Ted	He'll choke. If it stung his throat it could block his windpipe.
Edna	No problem. I knew that onion would come in handy. Try this young man. [*She puts a chunk of onion in his mouth*] That'll take away the swelling. You can't beat raw onion.
Thug	Ughaaaah . . . eeeeh . . . oooooh . . . umph . . .
Ted	He's gone a funny colour. I think he's crying. Look at the tears. He's not so tough after all.
Thug	I'm getting out of here. I hate you. I hate the world. Most of all – I hate onions! You're mad. You're crazy. You're off your rocker. You're round the bend, up the pole, round the twist.

27

I'm the only one round here with any sense.
[*He grabs the sack and jumps out of the door to a splash and a spray of water*] Aaaaaaaaaaaaaah!

Ted   Not that clever. He didn't know we're at sea.

Edna   But not for long – look. It's the pier. We're about to hit it.

Ted   There are people waiting for us with a rope and ... the police and ... a TV camera.

Edna   Ooh, Ted – we'll be on the News.

Ted   And look – by heck, it's ... it's ... [*He faints*]

Edna   It's Anna Bruce – your heart-throb! With the News crew. I'll have to take a photo. [*FLASH*] After all, everyone will be so amazed. No one will believe me when I show them!

Treading the Boards

Scene: Ted and Edna are in a TV studio for a live broadcast of 'Crime Bust', presented by Anna Bruce. There is music before Anna talks to the camera.

Anna	Good evening and welcome to another 'Crime Bust', where you, the public, help to solve crimes. We start tonight's live programme with a report on the story in the News about a robbery and kidnap. We are pleased to say that an arrest has been made, thanks to our two guests tonight. Ted and Edna Plunge are heroes. Perhaps I could start with you, Ted. Weren't you lucky to get out of this alive?
Ted	Yes, Anna.
Anna	In fact, when I first saw you on the pier, I had to help give you first aid, didn't I?
Ted	Yes, Anna.
Anna	What will you remember most about all of this?
Ted	You giving me the kiss of life. It nearly killed me.
Anna	But what do you remember about the crime? How did you come to be floating in the sea in your little beach hut?

Ted	The storm washed us out to sea. If it wasn't for Edna's pastry, we would have sunk. She makes jam puffs, you see.
Anna	So when did the robber strike?
Ted	It was after I found a body in the roof of the beach hut.
Edna	Ted popped up to fiddle with our TV aerial but a wasp went in the sugar and he got tangled in his vest . . .
Ted	And there she was – all tied up. So we did a bit of first aid with our ABC and an onion. She's as right as rain now.
Anna	I'm not sure if our viewers are following all of this! Yet I'm pleased to say that the Group Ten van driver is well and back at work – thanks to Ted and Edna. Edna, if I can turn to you. I think you took some photos and you have them here.
Edna	Yes – they're here in my bag with a bit of onion and a jam puff. They're mixed with our holiday snaps . . . This one here is our hotel last year. Very nice with lovely curtains. And this one shows my late sister . . .
Anna	I'm sorry to hear she's died.
Edna	Oh, she hasn't. She just can't get to things on time. Here she is on holiday in Blackpool.

Anna	Very nice. I didn't know they had seals on the beach there.
Edna	They don't. That's my sister in her wet suit. Ah, here we are. This is the young thug who tried to shoot us.
Anna	He looks very mean and ugly, with a horrible swollen face.
Edna	No, not that one. That's Ted eating one of my jam puffs.
Ted	Edna's jam puffs are a bit on the chewy side, you see . . .
Anna	But am I right in thinking that one of them saved your life?
Ted	Yes, Anna. If that thug hadn't taken a bite and been stung by a wasp, Edna and I would have been shot.
Anna	I hear the robber has tried to sue you, Edna. Is that true?
Edna	Yes. He says I put a wasp in my jam puff. I didn't mean to.
Anna	In fact, we have proof that Edna is right. For the first time on live TV, we are able to show what really happened.
Ted	Yes, Anna. We didn't know at the time, but when Edna put the video camera up on the shelf it was still filming. We have a video of it all.

Anna	Let's just take a look. This is how it started. Edna, can you talk us through this clip?
Edna	Well there we are, spinning round in the sea in our little beach hut. We are trying to help the woman driver who we found in the roof – when suddenly the thug jumps down with a gun and shouts:

[*A replay of part of Act 2*]

Thug	[*Dropping down between them and waving a gun*] SHUT IT!
Edna	Told you, Ted.
Ted	Well I never.
Thug	Oi, did you hear me?
Edna	That's not very polite, young man.
Thug	I said, SHUT IT!
Edna	Have you been asleep up there?
Thug	FREEZE!
Ted	Telling me, it's right chilly.
Thug	I said, FREEZE!

[*Replay pauses*]

Anna	At this point, we'll freeze the action and just look at the robber's face as he begins to lose his temper.

[*Replay continues*]

Thug	Listen, you old bag – I'll blast you into the sky if you don't shut up. This gun is loaded.
Ted	It looks like he doesn't want sugar, Edna.
Edna	He's very rude. You won't get a biscuit if you speak like that.
Thug	SHUT UP! You old fools are in the middle of big trouble. If you poke your nose in a wasp's nest, you get stung.
Edna	Oh yes, talking of wasps, one was in here somewhere . . .
Thug	So now you've been stupid enough to poke your fat noses into my hideout, you'll get stung all right. You'll get DEAD!

[*Replay pauses*]

Anna   [*Talking to camera*] I wonder what you would do faced by such a threat. Well, Ted and Edna kept their cool. We now fast-forward the tape to see what happened a few minutes later . . .

[*The action can be mimed – played speeded up*]

We reach the point where Ted has been told to go up into the roof again to bring down a sack of stolen money. We see him hanging by his braces from a nail in the roof . . .

[*Replay continues*]

Edna	Are you sure I can't press you to a nice fresh jam puff?
Ted	Aaah! [*He hangs by his braces*] I'm sort of stuck.
Thug	That's it! I've had enough. You stupid old fool. You idiot, you dope head, block head [*thumping the table with each insult*], numskull, dip head, dumbell, pea brain, fat head, thick head, bone head, clod head . . . I HATE YOU!
Edna	Mind your language, young man.
Ted	And mind that table.

[*Replay pauses*]

Anna	Now watch what happens next. We've slowed down the tape for you to see clearly what happens . . .

[*In slow motion, with slow, deep voices*]

Thug	[*Shouting angrily*] I hate you and your naf beach hut. I hate your stupid tin-pot world with its cups of tea and jam puffs. This world is full of boring old twits like you who do nothing!
Ted	We're on holiday.
Thug	I want power, freedom and money. I want to be cool. That's why I kill – why I'm about to mow you down and wipe you out. I'm tough. I'm smart. I've got bottle.

Edna	I bet you haven't got the nerve to eat a whole jam puff.
Thug	SHUT UP! Why aren't you shaking with fear? I'll show you who's boss. I'll make you beg me for mercy. And yes, you stupid old crow – I'll easily eat one of your damn puffs.
Edna	JAM puffs. No need to swear.

[*Replay pauses*]

Anna And now we'll rewind a little bit of that clip for you to see clearly what happens . . . Just watch that little black dot in the top of the picture as it lands on the jam puff. It's the wasp. Watch now as we fast-forward the tape to the point where the robber takes a bite – just before he shouts . . .

[*Thug bites the jam puff, with the wasp on the top*]

So you see, Edna did not put a wasp inside the jam puff! The robber fell to the floor but Edna saved his life. How?

Edna With an onion. I always carry one in my handbag.

Anna Why's that?

Edna Just in case. If you ever get stung by a bee or a wasp, rub it with a raw onion. It might make you smell like a hamburger, but it helps stop the swelling.

Anna	With that piece of advice, we have to take a break now. Join us for Part Two when we ask you to phone in to the programme.
	[*Turning to Ted*] That's it – we're off air now.
Ted	Have we finished? Do we have to go now?
Anna	No, we'd like you to stay till the end of the programme.
Edna	I think Ted would like your autograph, Anna.
Anna	And I would like his. He's a hero. In fact, I'm just getting news that our switchboard is jammed with phone calls.
Ted	Jammed? A bit like Edna's puffs!
Anna	Everyone is phoning to say how great they think you are! You're both stars. They all want to make Edna's jam puffs. How about doing your own cooking programme: 'Ready Steady Plunge!'
Ted	By heck – fancy being on telly with Anna Bruce.
Edna	Wait till I tell them next door.
Anna	My boss also wants your autograph – on a contract. He's just phoned to say that he wants to sign you up for your own show. They all love you. 'The Ted and Edna Show'. Can you start next week?
Edna	Ooh, that sounds fun, Ted.
Ted	I'll have to get a new vest.

Anna	I'll speak to you about it later. We're about to start Part Two.
Edna	I've got my camera here. Can I take a photo of you two?
Anna	Please do. Come and sit next to me, Ted.
Ted	Shall we shake hands and smile at the camera?
Anna	No – how about a nice big kiss? [*They kiss as the camera flashes*]
Edna	I knew that would happen. Ted has fainted. It's all too much for him. He's slumped over Anna's desk.
Anna	Look out, we're back on air. [*Music starts*] [*Talking to camera*] Hello and welcome back to Part Two of 'Crime Bust'. This is where we show you faces of people wanted by the police. First, here is a man who has brought fear to a whole town . . .

[*Ted suddenly sits up on the desk*]

Ted	That was the best kiss I've had for years!
Edna	[*FLASH*] And that will make a great picture.
Ted	And just remember viewers – don't have nightmares! [*He slumps back on the desk*]
Anna	I seem to have lost my script. In fact, I haven't got a clue where we are! The Plunges have taken over the show!

Edna   Never mind, viewers. I've just finished my film so I'll pop out to Boots to get it done and I'll be back to show you my snaps in Part Three. Let's face it, no one will believe me when I show them. Just think, you can now see us live on TV. Whatever next? 'Plunge – The Musical' at a theatre near you? Stay tuned. We'll be back!